SING FOR CHRISTMAS

SING FOR CHRISTMAS

A Round of Christmas Carols
and
Stories of the Carols
by
Opal Wheeler

ILLUSTRATED BY

Gustaf Tenggren

BOOKS, INC.
Distributed by
New York, E. P. Dutton and Company, Inc., 1943

For
Mother and Father
and their Merry Children
who loved to
sing for Christmas

INDEX OF STORIES

INDEX OF MUSIC

SING FOR CHRISTMAS

THE FIRST CHRISTMAS CAROL

THE day before Christmas dawned crisp and clear, and the pale gold Italian sunshine lighted the ancient Roman highway where the good monk, St. Francis, and his little band of followers had been journeying since long before daybreak.

"A song, my little Brown Brothers," called the faithful saint. " 'Twill help to shorten our journey."

"And you shall have a new chant, good master," answered tall, kindly John. "And it will be of the Christmas season. Harken, Brothers – I will mark the beginning."

His rich, deep voice rang out in the early morning stillness, telling of the Christ Child born in Bethlehem, long, long ago. At the little refrain, the Brown Brothers joined in heartily, stepping the rhythm of the lovely, simple melody as they swung merrily along the highway.

But the clear brown eyes of St. Francis became sorely troubled, and when the song of joy was ended, he stopped under an old tree to rest.

"Little Brown Brothers, my heart is filled with great sadness that here in our own beloved land, the people have forgotten the birth of the Christ Child."

Quietly the young monks gathered around him.

"Have courage, master," they comforted.

"Ah, my brothers, your song has helped me to find a way to make them remember."

"Tell us, good master!"

"Very well, for I shall need your help. Yonder lies the village of Grecia, where we shall spend the blessed night of the Nativity. If we can arrive there in time, we may perform the

miracle that will help the people to understand the meaning of Christmas."

With glad hearts, the eager monks quickened their steps and arriving at the quaint old church, they worked with such speed, that when the purple shadows had deepened into Christmas Eve, the little crêche near the altar was finished.

"Ring the bell, good brothers! It is time to call the people of Grecia," commanded St. Francis.

With silvery tones, the chimes rang out in the starry night, and wonderingly, the village folk made their way to the church to gaze in awe at the little manger scene.

Holding their candles high to light the simple crêche, the Brown Brothers sang joyously their Christmas song, made that day on the Roman highway, and soon the villagers joined in heartily, their long torches making the little church as bright as day.

St. Francis stood close by, his heart overflowing with gladness as, through the long night, he kept watch over the Babe in the manger.

Brother John, seeing the peace and happiness of the master, closed his eyes to rest, and lo! the most wonderful dream came to him, of St. Francis bending over the crib. His great love awakened the Child, who smilingly stretched forth his hands and was gathered into the arms of the good saint.

The crêche of St. Francis, in the little village of Grecia, was the first ever made in this world, and the song sung that night by the little Brown Brothers, was the first Christmas carol ever heard on this earth, more than twelve hundred years ago.

In a little cottage on the edge of the deep forest in Saxony, there lived a kindly peasant named Hans Luther and his good wife, Margaret. They were very poor folk, and all day long, Hans worked hard cutting slate in the deep quarry to earn a meager living for his wife and small son, Martin.

There was very little time to be with the beautiful, fair-haired boy, and Hans was very sad, for he loved his son dearly.

"Wife, our Martin must have a better place in the world than I, when he grows to be a man."

"Yes, good husband. And he is such a quiet boy, and so thoughtful. If only there was a way to send him to a school, how much he would learn."

When Martin grew older, he loved to go on adventures in the deep, dark forest. How proud and happy he was when luck was with him, and he could bring home a nice fat rabbit or a plump bird, to toss into the pot for a fine tasty dinner!

At last the time came when a way was found to send Martin to school, and the Luther cottage was filled with busy preparations. Mother Luther hurried about, making ready the poor little bag of clothing. At least it could be neat and clean.

With a cheery good-by, Martin started off for the choir school in Eisenach, where his lodging was to be given him in return for singing in the church. But there was no money for food, so Martin was given permission to sing in the streets, and beg for food at the house doors of the town.

It was not long before the rich Frau Cotta noticed the young choir boy with the beautiful voice. But how hungry he looked! Something must be done at once. Earnestly she spoke to her husband, and in a short time, Martin was living at the Cotta home, where for three happy years there was good food, and a warm bed to sleep in.

The masters in the school were very proud of the fine young choir student, and when Martin went on to the University of Ehrfurt to earn the highest honors there, they were delighted with the good news.

Martin loved to study the Bible, and in later years he wrote it all in the language of the people so that they could read it easily. He became one of the greatest leaders and preachers in all the world, telling stories from his beloved Bible.

But more than anything else, Martin Luther longed to have the people sing in church, so he set to work to write music for them. When the hymns were ready, he taught them to the people, his heart glowing with pride and joy as the strong, stirring melodies rang through the small building.

Now the children must have music, too. Perhaps he had better write something for his own little ones, first. Just before Christmas, the loveliest poem came into his mind:

Away in a manger
No crib for his bed,
The little Lord Jesus
Lay down His sweet head.

The stars in the heavens
Looked down where He lay,
The little Lord Jesus
Asleep on the hay.

How the children loved the song that Father Luther had written especially for them! The little house rang joyously with their clear, glad voices. And even to this day, throughout all the world, children still love to sing the gentle Christmas hymn, "Away in a Manger."

Away in a Manger

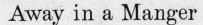

MARTIN LUTHER

MARTIN LUTHER

1. A - way in a man - ger, no crib for his bed, The
2. The cat - tle are low - ing, the ba - by a - wakes, But
3. Be near me, Lord Je - sus, I ask Thee to stay Close

lit - tle Lord Je - sus lay down his sweet head; The
lit - tle Lord Je - sus no cry - ing he makes, I
by me for - ev - er And love me, I pray; Bless

stars in the heav - ens Look'd down where he lay, The
love thee, Lord Je - sus, Look down from the sky, And
all the dear chil - dren in Thy ten - der care, And

lit - tle Lord Je - sus a - sleep on the hay.
stay by my cra - dle till morn - ing is nigh.
take us to heav - en to live with Thee there.

O LITTLE TOWN OF BETHLEHEM

EVERY morning early, what a scurrying there was in the old white house in Boston, as Agnes and Toodie and Gertie ran to see if the postman had left a letter from their uncle, Phillips Brooks. Especially Gertie, who loved him far more than anyone else in all the world.

One crisp November day, a sharp click told her that there was a letter in the post box! If only it was from Uncle Phillips, far away in Vienna, where he had gone for a little visit!

Yes, there was her name on the envelope, and eagerly tearing it open, she read:

Vienna, Nov. 19

Very PRIVATE!!

Dear Gertie, — This letter is an awful secret between you and me. If you tell anyone about it, I will not speak to you all this winter. And this is what it is about. You know Christmas is coming, and I am afraid that I shall not get home by that time, and so I want you to go and get the Christmas presents for the children. The grown people will not get any from me this year. But I do not want the children to go without, so you must find out, in the most secret way, just what Agnes and Toodie would most like to have, and get it and put it in their stockings and be very much surprised when you find it there. Will you do all this for me? But do not dare to let any of the children know of it until Christmas time. Then you can tell me in your Christmas letter just how you have managed about it all. Be a good girl, and do not study too hard, and keep our secret.

Your affectionate uncle   PHILLIPS

Phillips Brooks was loved by everyone, far and near, and people hurried to his church to hear him speak, for he was one of the greatest preachers in all the country.

But through his whole life, more than anything else, Phillips Brooks longed to go to Bethlehem to see the place where the Christ Child was born. Then one day his dearest wish came true, when he climbed the moonlit hills of Palestine, on Christmas Eve. Turning, he looked down on the little village nestling at his feet and thought of the blessed night when the little baby was born there in a manger, so many years ago.

Slowly he made his way down the hill, his heart filled with wonder. He would never forget this night.

At home in his study in America, he could see again the peaceful, starlit Palestine, and as he sat there at his desk, a beautiful poem came to him. Lovingly he put the words on paper: "O little town of Bethlehem,   How still we see thee lie."

Perhaps his young organist could set the poem to music. Eagerly Phillips Brooks hurried to the church.

"Redner, here is a little Christmas poem. Could you write music for it, so that the children could have a new song?"

"But there is so little time before the Christmas service!"

Hurrying away with the paper, Lewis Redner tried to think of a melody. But search as he would, the music would not come, and putting the paper away, he went sadly to bed.

The early dawn was just breaking when suddenly he awoke, a melody singing itself in his mind. Down went the notes, and just in time for the children to sing!

Phillips Brooks sat at the back of the church, listening joyously to the clear, sweet voices singing the new carol, "O Little Town of Bethlehem." But little did he know that some day, all the world would be singing his beautiful carol, telling of the coming of the Christ Child to earth.

O Little Town of Bethlehem

PHILLIPS BROOKS

LEWIS H. REDER

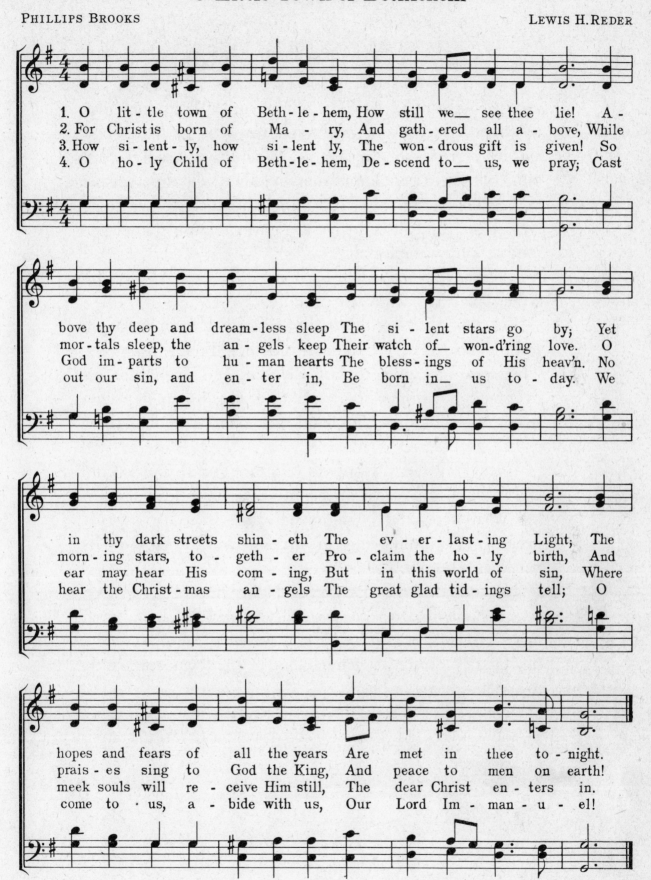

1. O lit-tle town of Beth-le-hem, How still we see thee lie! A-bove thy deep and dream-less sleep The si-lent stars go by; Yet in thy dark streets shin-eth The ev-er-last-ing Light; The hopes and fears of all the years Are met in thee to-night.

2. For Christ is born of Ma-ry, And gath-ered all a-bove, While mor-tals sleep, the an-gels keep Their watch of won-d'ring love. O morn-ing stars, to-geth-er Pro-claim the ho-ly birth, And prais-es sing to God the King, And peace to men on earth!

3. How si-lent-ly, how si-lent-ly, The won-drous gift is given! So God im-parts to hu-man hearts The bless-ings of His heav'n. No ear may hear His com-ing, But in this world of sin, Where meek souls will re-ceive Him still, The dear Christ en-ters in.

4. O ho-ly Child of Beth-le-hem, De-scend to us, we pray; Cast out our sin, and en-ter in, Be born in us to-day. We hear the Christ-mas an-gels The great glad tid-ings tell; O come to us, a-bide with us, Our Lord Im-man-u-el!

IN THE Southampton home of Schoolmaster Watts, long over two hundred years ago, there was born a little fair-haired boy, and his parents called him Isaac. When Isaac was five years old, he began to learn Latin from his father, who was a teacher in the school near by. In a short time, the small student could read in the difficult language so rapidly, that his father and mother were well pleased.

"Perhaps our son will be a schoolmaster some day, like his father," said Mother Watts, proudly.

But more than learning Latin, Isaac liked to sit at the old piano in one corner of the living room and make up pieces. They were very quiet, tuneful melodies, and his mother was delighted. She stopped her work to sit near the small player, struggling with parts of his gentle music that would not come right.

As he grew older, Isaac was very thoughtful, and so kind and sweet-natured, that his parents could not help wondering what he would be some day. But Isaac had already decided. He would be a great minister and preach to many people in a big church.

He studied harder than ever and when he was just twenty-six, he was invited to be the pastor of the Market Lane Church in the great city of London! Never was he so happy as on the first Sunday morning when he stood before the people, ready to speak to them.

But alas for poor Isaac! In a very few years he became quite ill, and was very sad when he had to leave the beautiful church that he loved so well. If only there were some way that he could still work for the people!

As he sat there thinking, an invitation came to him from his old friend, Sir Thomas Abney, asking him to spend a week at his beautiful home in the country. Eagerly Isaac Watts set out, and when he arrived at the Abney home, his heart was filled with joy at the beauties of the wide-spreading park with its birds and trees and wild flowers.

Suddenly a lovely poem came into his mind and he hurried to write it down. And now, if only the words could be set to music, all the people would have a hymn to sing! Each day there were more and more fine poems, and carefully Watts set them all down until there was no more room in the big book.

The happy week at the fine old estate went quickly by, and he was invited to stay on as long as he wished. The weeks grew into months, and instead of spending one week with his friend, Watts stayed on for thirty-five years, making Abney Park his home.

His poems grew and grew, and how delighted he was when musicians and composers set them all to music. Now there were more than six hundred hymns for the people to sing. Isaac Watts's dearest wish had come true and he became known as the Father of Hymnody.

For his stirring "Joy to the World," Edward Hodges wrote some fine music. But later, our own American musician, Lowell Mason, took the words and set them to music written by the great composer, Handel. And now, people in many lands sing "Joy to the World" with this beautiful music.

Joy to the World! the Lord is Come

Issac Watts

George F. Handel
Arr. by Lowell Mason

O COME, ALL YE FAITHFUL

It was late Christmas Eve in France, and from their quiet home, the good monks gathered together under the stars, ready to march to the little church among the hills where they were to worship the Christ Child at the midnight service, called a mass.

Long they had waited for this holy night, the most blessed of all the year, and when the last, brown-robed monk took his place in the processional, all was in readiness. Slowly they began to wind over the quiet hillside, their tall, flickering torches lighting the rugged pathway.

At the head of the long line, tall Brother John began to sing the Latin song, "O Come, All Ye Faithful," the monks joining heartily in the beautiful Christmas hymn.

How their voices rang out in the clear, starry night, more than two hundred years ago! And how our voices still ring out as we sing this fine old Christmas song when the festival season comes round.

No one knows who wrote the words. The music is an old Latin hymn, born somewhere in France. This stirring "O Come, All Ye Faithful" is sung by more people than any other Christmas song that has ever come down to us. It has been made into more than one hundred and twenty different languages so that all people everywhere may sing it.

O Come, All Ye Faithful

Latin Hymn

1. O come, all ye faith-ful, Joy-ful and tri-umph-ant, O
2. Sing, choirs of an - gels, Sing in ex-ul - ta - tion,
3. Yea, Lord, we greet Thee, Born this hap-py morn-ing

come ye, O come ye to Beth - le - hem;
Sing, all ye cit - i - zens of heav'n a - bove:
Je - sus, to Thee be glo - ry giv'n:

Come and be - hold Him, Born the King of an - gels;
Glo - ry to God In the high - est;
Word of the Fa - ther, Now in flesh ap - pear - ing;

After each verse

O come, let us a - dore Him, O come, let us a -

dore Him, O come, let us a - dore Him, Christ, the Lord.

35

DECK THE HALL

THERE was never a jollier time in all the world than at Yule Tide in England and the North Countries, long, long ago, even before our Christmas was dreamed of. To be sure, it was at the same time of year as our own Christmas, and many of the things that they did then are still enjoyed to this day.

What preparations there were for the happy season! First of all, there was the Yule Log to be cut. And it must be the stoutest and greenest tree in all the deep wood, for the festival season would last only as long as the great log burned – even down to the smallest cinder. Perhaps it would last for seven whole days, or even ten, and by luck, for as much as two whole weeks.

Then there was the holly and the ivy and the mistletoe to be cut to decorate the hall, to the singing of "Deck the hall with boughs of holly." And, of course, there were the mince pies and plum puddings, and the wassail bowl to be prepared.

At last, when all was in readiness, what a celebration took place! The great oaken doors of the hall were opened wide, and with mighty shouts, the Yule Log was dragged in. Solemnly each member of the family and all of the guests in turn, sat on the log to make a good wish. Then, with much ceremony, it was placed in the wide open hearth and lighted, to the singing of the second verse of "Deck the Hall" – "See the blazing Yule before us."

The dancing and feasting and merrymaking began, and, until late into the night and every night while the Yule Log blazed, the great hall resounded with singing, especially the favorite carol, "Deck the Hall."

Everyone was a little sad when it came time to sing the last verse, "Fast away the old year passes," for it meant that soon the Yule Log would be burned away, and then it would be a whole year before they could sing "Deck the Hall" again.

And to this very day, this old, old song from Wales is one of our favorite carols that we love to sing at Christmas time all the world over.

There was the holly and the ivy and the mistletoe to be cut to decorate the hall.

The Yule Log must be the stoutest and greenest tree in all the deep wood.

Deck the Hall

Traditional

Old Welsh Air

1. Deck the hall with boughs of hol - ly, Fa, la, la, la, la, la, la, la, la.
2. See the blaz - ing Yule be - fore us, Fa, la, la, la, la, la, la, la, la.
3. Fast a - way the old year pass - es, Fa, la, la, la, la, la, la, la, la.

'Tis the sea - son to be jol - ly, Fa, la, la, la, la, la, la, la, la.
Strike the harp and join the cho - rus, Fa, la, la, la, la, la, la, la, la.
Hail the new, ye lads and lass - es, Fa, la, la, la, la, la, la, la, la.

Don we now our gay ap - par - rel, Fa, la, la, la, la, la, la, la, la,
Fol - low me in mer - ry meas - ure, Fa, la, la, la, la, la, la, la, la,
Sing we joy - ous all to - geth - er, Fa, la, la, la, la, la, la, la, la,

Troll the an - cient Yule - tide car - ol, Fa, la, la, la, la, la, la, la, la.
While I tell of Yule - tide treas - ure, Fa, la, la, la, la, la, la, la, la.
Heed - less of the wind and weath - er, Fa, la, la, la, la, la, la, la, la.

THE HOLLY AND THE IVY

IN VERY early times, long before the Christ Child was born, people made carols about trees and flowers and birds, because they loved and worshipped these beautiful things in the nature world around them. As they sang their simple songs, gaily-dressed maidens danced on the green with the young men of the village. The maidens were called the Ivy, and the young men, the Holly.

Now in one of these villages, in ancient days, there lived an English knight who was very lonely. His children had long since left the towering castle, and when the festival time of the year came round, there was no one to celebrate in the great old hall.

Something must be done, and at once. Calling his servant to him, the good knight commanded:

"Go to all the people living on my lands – rich and poor alike, and bid them dine with me on Christmas day."

"Yes, master."

The tenants were delighted with the good news. What a fine surprise! To dine in the castle of the great knight! Out came the best doublet and hose and ribbons and laces, and on Christmas day, one and all danced along the highway to the castle on the hill.

What a sight met their eyes when the heavy doors were flung open! There in the great hall, the long oak table was groaning with roast pig and duckling, mince pies and plum puddings, and every fine dish that one could dream about for long years to come!

When the last guest was seated, the old knight arose, a twinkle in his eye.

"My good neighbors, hear me," said he. "Before you shall eat or drink at this board, you must prove yourselves worthy. Holly, whoever among you is master of his wife, shall now take his stand and carol for the assembled company."

There was long silence. Could it be, then, that in all this company, not even one Holly was master of his wife?"

At last from his place a youth arose and, stuttering and stammering, sang a few measures in a weak, quavering voice. As he sank back into his seat, loud laughter rang throughout the hall. The knight was highly amused and rising, bowed to the women.

"Ivy, 'tis now your turn. Whichever of you is master of her husband, let her sing a carol as proof."

At once, every maiden sprang to her feet and such a singing arose as was never before heard in all the land! The old knight rolled with laughter and, rapping on the floor with his stout cane, shouted merrily,

"The Ivy! The Ivy is the master!"

This old carol, with French melody and English words, was printed in England on sheets called "Broadsides," for all the people to sing.

The Holly and the Ivy

Traditional

1. The hol-ly and the i-vy Now both are full well grown; Of all the trees that are in the wood, The hol-ly bears the crown.
2. The hol-ly bears a blos-som, As white as lil-y flower; And Ma-ry bore sweet Je-sus Christ, To be our sweet Sav-iour.
3. The hol-ly bears a ber-ry As red as an-y blood; And Ma-ry bore sweet Je-sus Christ, To do poor sin-ners good.
4. The hol-ly bears a prick-le, As sharp as an-y thorn; And Ma-ry bore sweet Je-sus Christ, On Christ-mas Day at morn.

O the ris-ing of the sun, The run-ning of the deer, The play-ing of the mer-ry or-gan, Sweet sing-ing in the choir, Sweet sing-ing in the choir.

5.	6.
The holly bears a bark,	The holly and the ivy
As bitter as any gall;	Now both are full well grown,
And Mary bore sweet Jesus Christ,	Of all the trees that are in the wood,
For to redeem us all.	The holly bears the crown

HERE WE COME A WASSAILING

CHRISTMAS EVE had come to England, and what a merry time it was for the bands of jolly young folk, gathered around the broad open hearths in shining farmhouse kitchens, to mix their wassail bowls of ale.

"A little pinch of spice, good Dickon."

"Aye, and have a great care – 'tis heating fast to the boiling point."

"Then pour it into the wooden bowl, for it is high time that we were off for the wassailing."

Shouting and laughing gaily, the merry revelers hurried away to the farmhouse of Neighbor Hoskins, just over the hill, the brightly-beribboned bowl held carefully before them, well covered to keep in the heat.

"Quiet, comrades, we are almost there!"

Creeping silently to the door, their eager young voices rang out in the keen, frosty air.

"Wassail! Wassail!" (We wish you good health)

Young farmer Dickon struck up the merry song, "Here We Come A-wassailing," and at the first joyous sound, the great oaken doors were flung wide.

"Wassail! Wassail!" welcomed smiling master and mistress Hoskins, drinking from the steaming bowl and bringing gifts to the delighted carollers.

On went the merrymakers to the next farmhouse, and throughout the twelve festival days, they mixed their spicy bowls of ale to drink wassail with their good neighbors over all the countryside. How sorry they were when the Yule Tide was ended and it was time to go back to their work on the farm!

There never could be Christmas in England without this jolly carol which was born there so many, many years ago that we do not even know who wrote it. And in some parts of the land, there is still the old custom of wassailing, though in most places there is just carolling, instead.

Many people like to begin this song with the words, "Here we come a-carolling," instead of "Here we come a-wassailing." But it may be sung whichever way you like it best.

Here We Come a-Wassailing

Traditional English

Moderato

1. Here we come a-was-sail-ing A-mong the leaves so
2. We are not dai-ly beg-gars That beg from door to
3. Good mas-ter and mis-tress, As you sit by the
4. God bless the mas-ter of this house, Like-wise the mis-tress,

green; Here we come a-wan-d'ring, So fair to be seen.
door; But we are neigh-bors' chil-dren, Whom you have seen be-fore.
fire, Pray think of us poor chil-dren, Who wan-der in the mire.
too, And all the lit-tle chil-dren, That round the ta-ble go.

REFRAIN

Love and joy come to you, And to you your was-sail too; And God bless you and

send you a hap-py New Year, And God send you a hap-py New Year.

47

THE FIRST NOWELL

Was there ever a lovelier carol in all the world than "The First Nowell"? It means "The First Christmas" and is one of the very oldest songs ever written about the coming of the King of Israel.

This carol is so old that no record can be found as to who wrote it or where it came from. There are some who believe it to be French, for it is said that the carol was first printed in France, and often we find it called "The First Noel." Others tell us that it came from England, and was given the name, "The First Nowell."

Perhaps it was sung by the shepherds themselves as they tended their sheep on the great open plains, stopping to gaze in wonder at the Christmas Star that suddenly shone over their heads in the silent night. The carol tells the story of the coming of the angels to the shepherds, proclaiming the birth of the Christ Child.

It is said that in olden times, the shepherds sang the verses, and from the heavens, the angels answered with the chorus:

"Nowell, Nowell, Nowell, Nowell,
Born is the King of Israel."

Now I know that on this very night, the Christ Child will be born unto you."

*   *   *

This ancient story of the cherry tree is one of the oldest in all the world and came to us from England. It was first of all a Mystery Play and was performed in the churches over five hundred years ago. Later, the words were set to a melody, perhaps a folk tune, and from that time on, the quaint "Cherry Tree Carol" has been sung in England and other countries every year at Christmas time.

The Cherry Tree Carol

English

Traditional

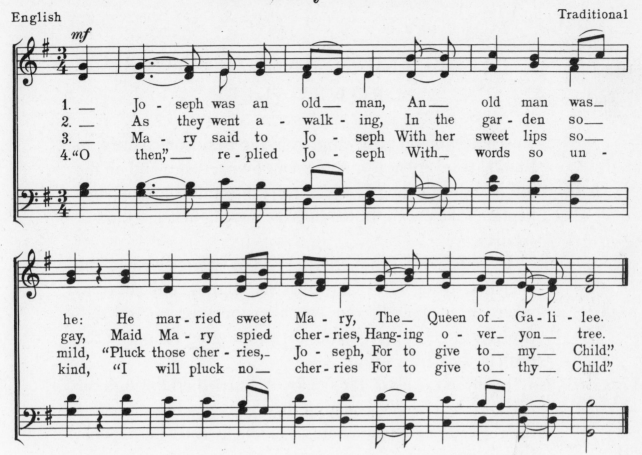

1. — Jo - seph was an old — man, An — old man was — he: He mar - ried sweet Ma - ry, The — Queen of — Ga - li - lee.
2. — As they went a - walk - ing, In the gar - den so — gay, Maid Ma - ry spied cher - ries, Hang-ing o - ver — yon — tree.
3. — Ma - ry said to Jo - seph With her sweet lips so — mild, "Pluck those cher - ries, — Jo - seph, For to give to — my — Child?"
4. "O then," — re - plied Jo - seph With — words so un - kind, "I will pluck no — cher - ries For to give to — thy — Child?"

5. Mary said to cherry tree,
"Bow down to my knee,
That I may pluck cherries
By one, two, and three."

6. The uppermost sprig then
Bowed down to her knee:
"Thus you may see, Joseph,
These cherries are for me?"

7. "O eat your cherries, Mary,
O eat your cherries now,
O eat your cherries, Mary,
That grow upon the bough."

8. As Joseph was a-walking
He heard angels sing,
This night there shall be born
Our heavenly King.

9. "He neither shall be born
In house nor in hall,
Nor in the place of Paradise,
But in an ox-stall."

10. "He shall not be clothed
In purple nor pall;
But all in fair linen,
As wear babies all."

11. "He shall not be rocked,
In silver nor gold,
But in a wooden cradle
That rocks on the mould."

12. "He neither shall be christened
In milk nor in wine,
But in pure spring-well water
Fresh sprung from Bethine."

13. Mary took her Baby,
She dressed Him so sweet,
She laid Him in a manger
All there for to sleep.

14. As she stood over Him
She heard Angels sing,
"Oh! bless our dear Savior,
Our heavenly King."

SHEPHERDS! SHAKE OFF YOUR DROWSY SLEEP

This beautiful old carol came from the Besancon country, in France. It is very near mountainous Switzerland; and on the soft hillsides, flowing gently in every direction, the shepherds kept their lonely vigils, tending their sheep in every kind of weather.

In very olden times, Mystery Plays were given in the churches, telling of the Christmas Star shining in the heavens where the shepherds were watching their sheep. And suddenly an angel appeared unto them, bringing tidings of the birth of the Christ Child.

In one of the plays, the shepherds hurried off through the night to the manger, bringing their gifts of a brooch with a little bell attached, two cobnuts on a ribbon, and a horn spoon, large enough to hold forty peas.

In another Mystery Play, one shepherd brought an oaten pipe; the second offered his hat as a gift; and the third, his mittens to keep the Child's hands warm.

There is an ancient carol over four hundred years old, called, "The Jolly Shepherd Wat." The good herd's boy hears the angel's message, and leaving his friends Mall and Will, goes off to Bethlehem to worship the Child. Arriving at the manger, he presents his gifts, saying:

> "Jesu, I offer to Thee here my pipe,
> My scrip, my tax-box and my skirt;
> Home to my fellows now will I skip,
> And also look unto my sheep."

We do not know who wrote the words or the melody of the carol, "Shepherds! Shake Off Your Drowsy Sleep." But Sir John Stainer, the beloved English organist and composer, took the melody and arranged it with an accompaniment for us to sing.

Shepherds! Shake off your Drowsy Sleep

Besancon Carol

1. Shep-herds! shake off your drow - sy sleep, Rise and leave your sil - ly sheep;
2. Hark! e - ven now the bells ring round, Lis - ten to their mer - ry sound;
3. See how the flow'rs all burst a - new, Think-ing snow is sum - mer dew;
4. Shep-herds! then up and quick a - way, Seek the Babe at break of day;

An-gels from heav'n a - round loud sing - ing, Ti-dings of__ great joy__ are bring-ing.
Hark! how the birds new songs are mak-ing, As_ if win-ter's chains were break-ing.
See how the stars a - fresh are glow-ing, All their bright-est beams be - stow-ing.
He is the hope of ev - 'ry na - tion, All in him shall find__ sal - va-tion.

CHORUS

Shep-herds! the cho - rus come and swell! Sing No - ël, Oh, sing_ No - ël.

59

Carol of the Birds

BAS-QUERCY

Moderato *mf*

1. Whence comes this rush of wings a - far,
2. "Tell us, ye birds, why come ye here,
3. Hark! how the green - finch bears his part,
4. An - gels and shep - herds, birds of the sky,

Fol - low - ing straight the No - el star?
In - to this sta - ble, poor and drear?
Phil - o - mel, too, with ten - der heart,
Come where the Son of God doth lie;

Birds from the woods in won - drous flight,
"Hast - 'ning we seek the new - born King,
Chants from her leaf - y dark re - treat,
Christ on earth with man doth dwell,

Beth - le - hem seek this Ho - ly Night.
And all our sweet - est mu - sic bring"
Re, mi, fa, sol, in ac - cents sweet.
Join in the shout, "No - el, No - el!"

Angels from the Realms of Glory

JAMES MONTGOMERY   HENRY SMART

1. An - gels from the realms of glo - ry, Wing your flight o'er
2. Shep - herds in the fields a - bid - ing, Watch - ing o'er your
3. Sag - es leave your con - tem - pla - tions; Bright - er vi - sions
4. Saints be - fore the al - tar bend - ing, Watch - ing long in

all the earth; Ye who sang cre - a - tion's sto - ry,
flocks by night; God with man is__ now re - sid - ing,
beam a - far: Seek the great De - sire of na - tions,
hope and fear, Sud - den - ly the__ Lord, de - scend - ing,

Now pro - claim Mes - si - ah's birth:
Yon - der shines the__ in - fant Light:
Ye have seen His__ na - tal star: Come and wor - ship,
In His tem - ple__ shall ap - pear:

come and wor - ship, Wor - ship Christ, the__ new - born King.

GOD REST YOU MERRY, GENTLEMEN

THROUGHOUT the whole of England, there is no carol so well loved as "God Rest You Merry, Gentlemen," which means, "God keep you merry, gentlemen." Just when this old, old carol was born, or who wrote the words, no one knows. Perhaps it is an old folk song, made by the people themselves to celebrate the Christmas season.

There are two well-known melodies for this carol, but the English people use this one, for they like it best. For many long years, when Christmas time came round, sheets called "Broadsides" with songs printed on them, were given to all the people so that they could sing carols in the streets.

The three carols on the sheets most widely sung were: "God Rest You Merry, Gentlemen," "I Saw Three Ships," and "The First Nowell."

Little villages, as well as great cities, rang with the glad voices of the people as they celebrated the festival season in Merry England, always ending with their favorite carol, "God Rest You Merry, Gentlemen."

God Rest You Merry, Gentlemen

Traditional

English Carol

Giojoso

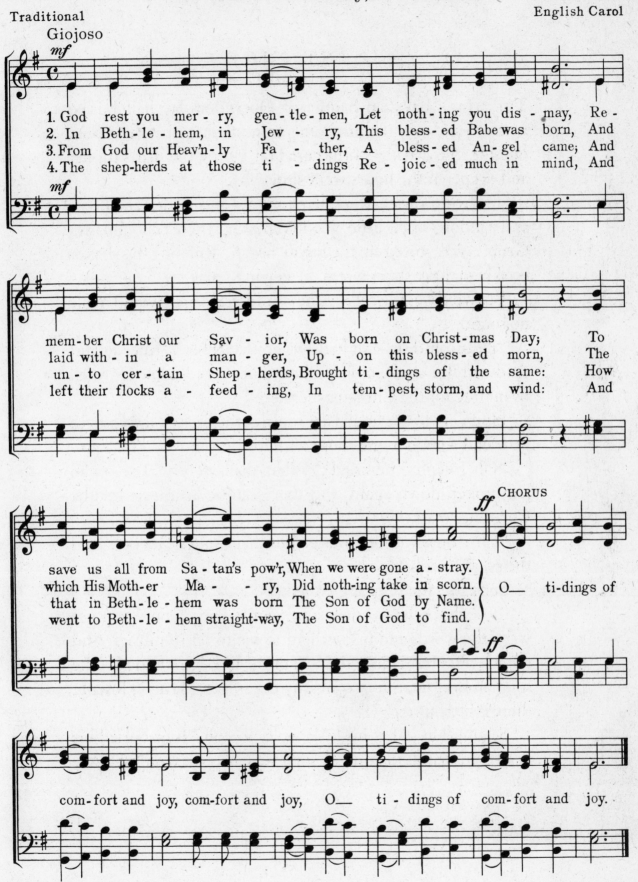

1. God rest you mer - ry, gen - tle - men, Let noth - ing you dis - may, Re -
2. In Beth - le - hem, in Jew - ry, This bless - ed Babe was born, And
3. From God our Heav'n - ly Fa - ther, A bless - ed An - gel came; And
4. The shep-herds at those ti - dings Re - joic - ed much in mind, And

mem - ber Christ our Sav - ior, Was born on Christ - mas Day; To
laid with - in a man - ger, Up - on this bless - ed morn, The
un - to cer - tain Shep - herds, Brought ti - dings of the same: How
left their flocks a - feed - ing, In tem - pest, storm, and wind: And

CHORUS

save us all from Sa - tan's pow'r, When we were gone a - stray.
which His Moth - er Ma - ry, Did noth - ing take in scorn. O— ti-dings of
that in Beth - le - hem was born The Son of God by Name.
went to Beth - le - hem straight-way, The Son of God to find.

com - fort and joy, com - fort and joy, O— ti - dings of com - fort and joy.

SILENT NIGHT

THE LITTLE Bavarian hamlet of Oberndorf lay half buried in snow, and over the tiny cottages, nestled against the mountainside, the driving storm raged on, piling the drifts higher and deeper as the hours went slowly by.

The wind shrieked in the chimneys and rattled the doors and windows of the little wooden church, where Schoolmaster Gruber was seated at the small organ. Rubbing his hands briskly to make them warm, he began to play.

But what was this? Try as he would, the organ would make no sound.

"Dear, oh dear," sighed Organist Gruber. "Mice again! And with the snow so deep, the repairman could never reach us in time for the Christmas service!"

Hurrying to the small bare room at the back of the church, he found a good monk, busy with his prayers.

"Oh Joseph," he cried, "What shall we do? The organ has broken down again, and there can be no music for the Christmas mass."

"Christmas without music? But that could never be!" said the good Joseph Mohr.

Suddenly the organist smiled.

"Joseph, perhaps a new song would help. Could you not write the words and bring them to me to set to music? And there is old Hermann at the foot of the hill. He could play the song on his guitar, to accompany the singers. Hurry, Joseph, there is little time."

Seating himself at his little table, Joseph Mohr buried his head in his hands to think. A song – a Christmas song! Slowly the words came to him and down on the paper they went.

"Silent night, holy night,   All is calm, all is bright."

When the last words were written, darkness had fallen, and off to the organist he hurried with the paper.

"The poem is good, my friend!" cried Gruber. "If only I can write a melody half as beautiful, we should be well pleased."

Soon he was humming a little tune, and slowly the music fitted the words. There! It was finished at last, and just in time to practice with old Hermann and the singers before the midnight mass.

Candles were lighted and, through the driving snow, the villagers came to listen to the Christmas Eve service. There, in front of the little church was Hermann, the cobbler, strumming simple chords while the quaint mountain singers lifted their fresh young voices in the lovely new song.

The storm outside was soon forgotten as the villagers drank in the beautiful music, so filled with peace and joy.

A few days later, the old repairman, busily at work on the organ, spied the new song, and when the last key was mended he had learned the carol by heart. Off he trudged through the great drifts of snow, singing "Silent Night" to his heart's content.

Soon his friends in the Austrian Tyrol were singing the fine carol, and when at last they set sail for America, they delighted the audiences there with their fine Tyrolian music, always ending with the new carol, "Silent Night."

And so our own American people came to hear the lovely song and have grown to love it more than any other Christmas carol, the beautiful "Silent Night, Holy Night."

The quaint little mountain singers lifted their fresh young voices in the lovely new song.

Off he trudged through the great drifts of snow, singing Silent Night to his heart's content.

Silent Night, Holy Night

JOSEPH MOHR

FRANZ GRÜBER

1. Si - lent night! Ho - ly night! All is — calm, all is — bright;
2. Si - lent night! Ho - ly night! Shep - herds quake at the — sight!
3. Si - lent night! Ho - ly night! Son of — God, love's pure — light

Round yon vir - gin moth - er and Child! Ho - ly In - fant, so ten - der and mild,
Glo - ries stream from heav - en a - far, Heav'n-ly hosts — sing Al - le - lu - ia:
Ra - diant beams from Thy ho - ly face, With the dawn of re - deem - ing grace,

Sleep in heav - en - ly peace, — Sleep in heav - en - ly peace. —
Christ, the Sav - iour is born! — Christ, the Sav - iour is born! —
Je - sus, Lord, at Thy birth, — Je - sus, Lord, at Thy birth. —

IN ENGLAND, in the year 1707, when the eighteenth child was born in the Wesley home, Father Wesley exclaimed,

"Another boy! But I have almost run out of names, good wife! What shall we call this new son of ours?"

Kind Mother Wesley thought hard for a moment.

"Let us call him Charles. Charles Wesley. It will be a fine, honest name for this little boy to grow up with."

But Charles came very near not growing up to use his good name, for when he was just two years old, a fire broke out in the old house, trapping him far off in one corner. But faithful Nurse Anna, rushing back into the building, wrapped the baby in a thick blanket and carried her favorite child to safety.

With so many children to be cared for in the simple Wesley home, there were hard times in the years that went swiftly by, and many times Charles had to struggle for himself.

The boys at the Westminster School grew very fond of him and made him their captain, for he was always fair and just. One day, as Captain Wesley was hard at work at his studies, a tall, handsomely-dressed stranger came to see him.

"Charles, I am your uncle, and I have come all the way from Ireland to ask you if you would come home to live with me and be my son," he said. "I am growing old and need someone to care for my lands. Some day they would all be yours and you would become one of the proudest and greatest rulers in all Ireland."

To have everything in the world that his heart could wish for! It was all too good to be true! Charles thought hard for a moment and, looking up at his fine uncle, he smiled.

"Thank you, sir, but I could not go home with you, for my Mother and Father will soon be needing my help."

Through the long hard years, Charles struggled on, determined to make a name for himself, alone. How proud and happy he was on the day that he became a minister, like his father!

But not long afterward, a new adventure came to him, when he sailed across the ocean with his brother John, to be secretary to the Governor of Georgia. But alas for poor Charles! Life was too difficult in this strange land and he became very ill.

There was nothing to do now but to go back to England, and soon he was ready to return to his beloved homeland.

It was a clear, sparkling day, and as the little boat sailed along, he listened contentedly to a little band of singers, their beautiful hymns ringing out over the water.

Perhaps he could write a hymn, too! The words came rapidly and, finding bits of paper in his pockets, he wrote them down. From that day on, his writing never ceased. Over six thousand hymns came from his pen, and he became known as the great hymn writer of all ages.

His beautiful "Hark, the Herald Angels Sing" was one of his favorites, and is still one of the favorites of all the world at Christmas time. The music for the hymn is a part of a festival song, written by the great composer, Mendelssohn, to celebrate the invention of printing.

The Englishman, Dr. Cummings, took the music and fitted the words of Charles Wesley's hymn to the lovely melody by Mendelssohn.

Hark! the Herald Angels Sing

CHARLES WESLEY

FELIX MENDELSSOHN-BARTHOLDY

1. Hark! the her-ald an-gels sing, "Glo-ry to the new-born King; Peace on earth, and mer-cy mild, God and sin-ners rec-on-ciled." Joy-ful, all ye na-tions, rise,— Join the tri-umph of the skies, With an-gel-ic hosts pro-claim, "Christ is born in Beth-le-hem."

2. Christ, by high-est heav'n a-dored, Christ, the ev-er-last-ing Lord: Come, de-sire of na-tions, come, Fix in us Thy hum-ble home. Veil'd in flesh the God-head see,— Hail th'in-car-nate De-i-ty!— Pleas'd as man with men to ap-pear, Je-sus our Im-man-uel here.

3. Hail the heav'n born Prince of Peace! Hail the Sun of right-eous-ness! Light and life to all He brings, Ris'n with heal-ing in His wings: Mild He lays His glo-ry by,— Born that man no more may die;— Born to raise the sons of earth; Born to give them sec-ond birth.

Hark! the her-ald an-gels sing, "Glo-ry to the new-born King."

GOOD KING WENCESLAS

THERE once lived in Bohemia, in the year 928, a wise and good nobleman named Duke Wenceslas. Now Duke Wenceslas ruled the people of his many broad lands with such wisdom and kindness that he became known as a saint.

No matter what hour of the day or night, if word were brought to him that one of his subjects was ill or in need, he hastened to send help at once. How the people loved their just ruler, Duke Wenceslas! And how gladly they obeyed the wishes of their noble leader.

When the Christmas season came round, Duke Wenceslas saw to it that it was celebrated in every church and cottage throughout the land. He loved the Christ Child and wanted his people to love Him, too.

This old, old carol from Bohemia tells a story about him and calls the good ruler, King Wenceslas, even though he was not a king. It tells of how the good Duke and his little page journeyed through deep drifts of snow on a cold, frosty night to bring food and fuel to a poor peasant, living far away under the mountain.

We do not know who wrote the words or the music of this fine old carol, but of all the carols of the Christmas season, there is none more loved than "Good King Wenceslas."

Good King Wenceslas

JOHN NEAL

Traditional

Allegro moderato

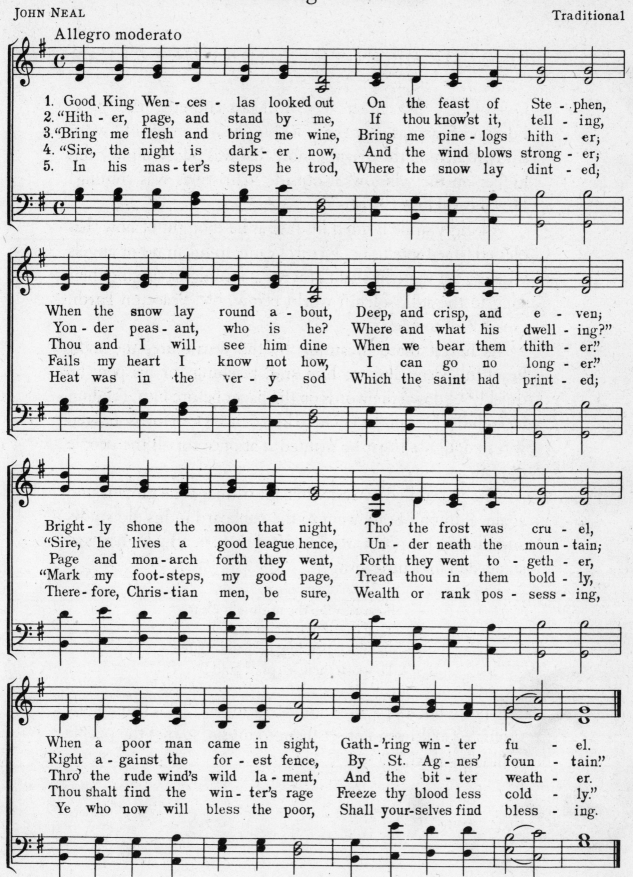

1. Good King Wen - ces - las looked out On the feast of Ste - phen,
2. "Hith - er, page, and stand by me, If thou know'st it, tell - ing,
3. "Bring me flesh and bring me wine, Bring me pine - logs hith - er;
4. "Sire, the night is dark - er now, And the wind blows strong - er;
5. In his mas - ter's steps he trod, Where the snow lay dint - ed;

When the snow lay round a - bout, Deep, and crisp, and e - ven;
Yon - der peas - ant, who is he? Where and what his dwell - ing?"
Thou and I will see him dine When we bear them thith - er."
Fails my heart I know not how, I can go no long - er."
Heat was in the ver - y sod Which the saint had print - ed;

Bright - ly shone the moon that night, Tho' the frost was cru - el,
"Sire, he lives a good league hence, Un - der neath the moun - tain;
Page and mon - arch forth they went, Forth they went to - geth - er,
"Mark my foot - steps, my good page, Tread thou in them bold - ly,
There - fore, Chris - tian men, be sure, Wealth or rank pos - sess - ing,

When a poor man came in sight, Gath - 'ring win - ter fu - el.
Right a - gainst the for - est fence, By St. Ag - nes' foun - tain."
Thro' the rude wind's wild la - ment, And the bit - ter weath - er.
Thou shalt find the win - ter's rage Freeze thy blood less cold - ly."
Ye who now will bless the poor, Shall your - selves find bless - ing.

79

ONE wintry December day in Massachusetts, the good Edmund Sears sat near the crackling hearth in his old worn study, watching the driving snow that was piling higher and higher on the windowsill outside. Christmas was coming! How he did love Christmas!

A kindly smile lighted his face as he thought of how that blessed time came to be. Pictures came to his mind of angels winging through the silent heavens at midnight, singing their song to the still, solemn world below, of "Peace on Earth, Good Will to Men."

As he sat there dreaming by the warm fire, the most beautiful poem came to him and, reaching for his pen, he quickly set down the words on the paper before him. Folding it carefully, he sent the poem to his friend, Dr. Morrison, who was so delighted that he printed it at once for all the people to read.

The year rolled by and when Christmas time came round again, Edmund Sears went to the cupboard in his old study, and finding his poem, read it aloud to a friend who had just stepped in for a little visit.

> "It came upon the midnight clear,
> That glorious song of old,
> Of angels bending near the earth
> To touch their harps of gold."

"Edmund, the words are so beautiful!" exclaimed the visitor. "Could you not set them to music, so that the people could sing them?"

The good minister laughed heartily.

"My dear friend, I am very sure that they would never care to sing a song that I had composed, for I cannot carry even the simplest tune! But you have given me an idea — a very good idea, indeed."

For a time he was lost in thought.

"I have it! Richard Willis, in Boston, is just the one to set my poem to music. I will send it off to him this very day. If only he can do it in time for Christmas, how happy I shall be!"

Off went the letter and when the musician, Richard Willis, read the note with the poem, he smiled. There was so little time, but he would try to write the music so that the song would be ready for Christmas. Never could he disappoint his old friend, Edmund Sears!

But a fine melody must be thought of, for so beautiful a poem. Slowly he read the words:

> "It came upon the midnight clear,
> That glorious song of old —"

Why, the lines almost sang themselves! Quickly he set to work and in a very short time the music was ready, simple and tuneful, and fitting the words so exactly.

Back went the song to the delighted Edmund Sears. It was indeed a beautiful carol for all the people to sing. And far across the water, in England, everyone loves as we do, the fine American carol, "It Came Upon the Midnight Clear."

It Came upon the Midnight Clear

Edmund H. Sears

Richard S. Willis

1. It came up-on the mid-night clear, That glo-rious song of old, From an-gels bend-ing near the earth, To touch their harps of gold: "Peace on the earth, good-will to men From heav'n's all gra-cious King," The world in sol-emn still-ness lay To hear the an-gels sing.

2. Still thro' the clo-ven skies they come, With peace-ful wings un-furl'd; And still their heav'n-ly mu-sic floats O'er all the wea-ry world: A-bove its sad and low-ly plains They bend on hov-'ring wing, And ev-er o'er its Ba-bel sounds The bless-ed an-gels sing.

3. For lo! the days are has-t'ning on, By proph-et bards fore-told, When with the ev-er-cir-cling years Comes round the age of gold, When peace shall o-ver all the earth Its an-cient splen-dors fling, And the whole world send back the song Which now the an-gels sing.

WE THREE KINGS

THE Christmas Star shed its piercing light over all the country-side, guiding the Three Kings far below on the moor, riding through the night on their patient camels, their rich, jeweled robes glowing with many colors.

Long days and nights they had been traveling over field and mountain, in search of the Christ Child.

Melchior, King of Nubia, with gray hair and long beard, held his precious casket of gold to present to the new-born Babe. Casper, the slender young King of Chaldea, carefully bore his gift of frankincense, a sweet-smelling incense to burn for the Christ Child. Tall, dark-skinned Balthazar eagerly carried aloft his tribute of myrrh, an incense made from the gum of balsam trees.

On to the West the great Star led them, until, weary from traveling, they came to the city of Jerusalem.

"Can you tell us where is He that is born King of the Jews?" they asked. "For we have seen His Star in the East, and have come to worship Him."

King Herod was much troubled when he heard the news. Was he not the King of Jerusalem? At once he sent for the chief priests of the people and questioned them closely.

"Where has this Christ Child been born?"

"In Bethlehem, as the prophets have written," they answered.

Then King Herod sent for the Three Wise Men, asking them when the Christmas Star had appeared to them in the heavens, saying:

"Go and search for the young Child, and when you have

found Him, bring me word, that I may go and worship Him also."

Once more the Three Kings set out on their way and lo! the Star which they saw in the East went before them to guide them and after many days, stopped over the simple dwelling of Mary and Joseph and the Christ Child.

Falling on their knees, they worshipped Him and offered their gifts of gold and frankincense and myrrh.

*   *   *

This beautiful old story from the Bible was made into a carol by the American minister, J. H. Hopkins, who wrote both the words and the music for "We Three Kings."

We Three Kings of Orient Are

J. H. HOPKINS   J. H. HOPKINS

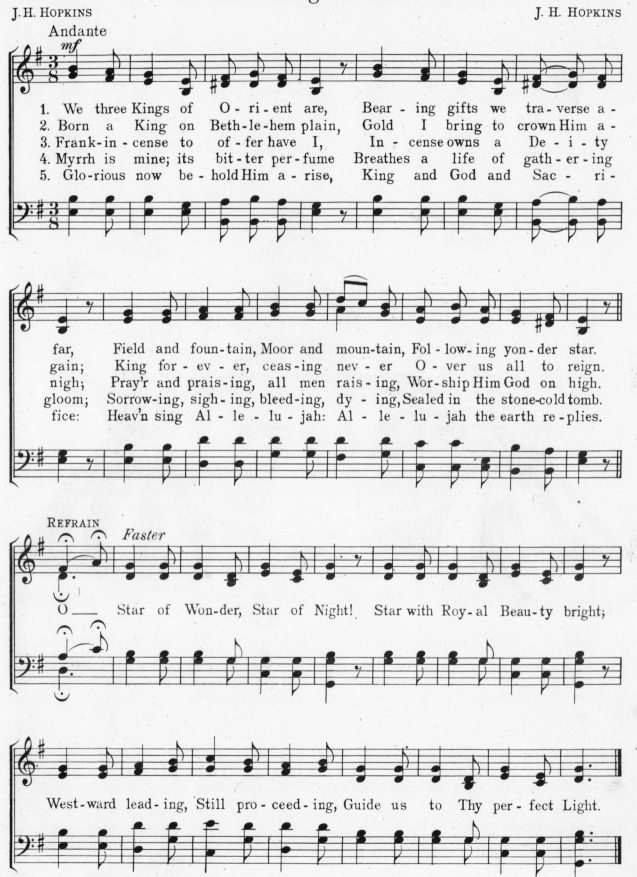

1. We three Kings of O - ri - ent are, Bear - ing gifts we tra - verse a -
2. Born a King on Beth - le - hem plain, Gold I bring to crown Him a -
3. Frank - in - cense to of - fer have I, In - cense owns a De - i - ty
4. Myrrh is mine; its bit - ter per - fume Breathes a life of gath - er - ing
5. Glo - rious now be - hold Him a - rise, King and God and Sac - ri -

far, Field and foun - tain, Moor and moun - tain, Fol - low - ing yon - der star.
gain; King for - ev - er, ceas - ing nev - er O - ver us all to reign.
nigh; Pray'r and prais - ing, all men rais - ing, Wor - ship Him God on high.
gloom; Sorrow - ing, sigh - ing, bleed - ing, dy - ing, Sealed in the stone - cold tomb.
fice: Heav'n sing Al - le - lu - jah: Al - le - lu - jah the earth re - plies.

REFRAIN *Faster*

O__ Star of Won - der, Star of Night! Star with Roy - al Beau - ty bright;

West - ward lead - ing, Still pro - ceed - ing, Guide us to Thy per - fect Light.

I SAW THREE SHIPS

CAROLS about Christmas have come to us from many countries. People living in cold, wintry climates have given us carols about pine trees and snow; those in warm countries gave us songs of flowers and birds; the hill towns tell of shepherds tending their sheep and journeying to the manger; and people living by the water have given us carols about ships bearing precious burdens.

And so this carol from England must have come from people living near the sea, telling us of three ships, one of them bearing Mary and the Christ Child. It is one of the three best loved carols in all England and is so old that no one knows who wrote either the words or the music.

But it may well have been a folk melody, and sung by the people as they danced on the village green, for it has such a delightful skipping rhythm.

I Saw Three Ships

Traditional English

4.
Pray, whither sailed those ships all three,
  On Christmas Day, on Christmas Day?
Pray, whither sailed those ships all three,
  On Christmas Day in the morning.

5.
O they sailed into Bethlehem,
  On Christmas Day, on Christmas Day;
O they sailed into Bethlehem,
  On Christmas Day in the morning.

6.
And all the bells on earth shall ring
  On Christmas Day, on Christmas Day;
And all the bells on earth shall ring
  On Christmas Day in the morning.

7.
And all the Angels in Heaven shall sing,
  On Christmas Day, on Christmas Day
And all the Angels in Heaven shall sing,
  On Christmas Day in the morning.

8.
And all the souls on earth shall sing,
  On Christmas Day, on Christmas Day;
And all the souls on earth shall sing,
  On Christmas Day in the morning.

9.
Then let us all rejoice amain,
  On Christmas Day, on Christmas Day;
Then let us all rejoice amain,
  On Christmas Day in the morning.

Carol of the Flowers

BAS-QUERCY

REFRAIN
mf

Come with us sweet flow'rs, and wor-ship Christ the—

Lord, Let your per-fumes hov-er round the Babe a-dored.

Fine

p

1. Mod-est vio-let, hid-ing in the grass-y
2. Lil-y fair, low bend-ing in the sun's warm
3. As thou, pan-sy, shin-eth forth in bright ar-
4. As thou, rose, wide op-'ning, doth thy scent im-

D.C.

shade, Thou canst say how hum-ble He for us is made.
light, Thou dost tell that He is pure as thou art white.
ray, So doth He His ma-jes-ty to man dis-play.
part, So His love ex-pand-ing, draws each sin-ful heart.

While Shepherds Watched Their Flocks

NAHUM TATE

Old English Melody

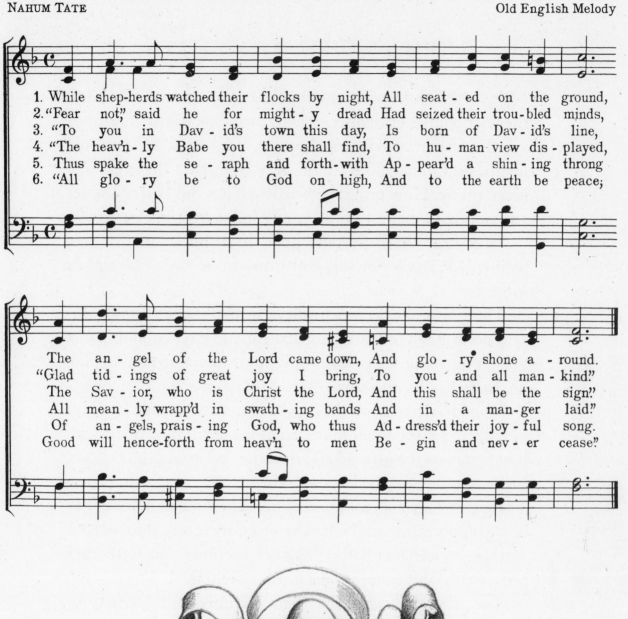

1. While shep-herds watched their flocks by night, All seat-ed on the ground,
2. "Fear not," said he for might-y dread Had seized their trou-bled minds,
3. "To you in Dav-id's town this day, Is born of Dav-id's line,
4. "The heav'n-ly Babe you there shall find, To hu-man view dis-played,
5. Thus spake the se-raph and forth-with Ap-pear'd a shin-ing throng
6. "All glo-ry be to God on high, And to the earth be peace;

The an-gel of the Lord came down, And glo-ry shone a-round.
"Glad tid-ings of great joy I bring, To you and all man-kind."
The Sav-ior, who is Christ the Lord, And this shall be the sign."
All mean-ly wrapp'd in swath-ing bands And in a man-ger laid."
Of an-gels, prais-ing God, who thus Ad-dress'd their joy-ful song.
Good will hence-forth from heav'n to men Be-gin and nev-er cease."

WHAT CHILD IS THIS?

No ONE could have been happier in all the great city of London than Schoolmaster Stainer, when, early one sunny morning, a little dark-eyed boy was born in his home. His parents named him John, and from the very beginning the small boy loved music. How proud he was when he could carry a tune, and sing with the rest of the family in his strong, clear voice.

"Just hear the little one, good husband," said Mother Stainer. "Perhaps our son will grow up to be a fine singer some day!"

There was always much music in the Stainer home, and as soon as his work was finished for the day, Schoolmaster Stainer hurried back to his simple, warm living room, to play his melodies on the small, sweet-toned organ.

John loved to play on the organ, too, and everyone laughed heartily to see the small musician in his short, neat frock, one foot firmly on the ground and the other pumping the bellows furiously, to make the keys sound.

Father Stainer spent much of his spare time in helping the boy with his music, and when he was only seven, John played and sang so well that Father Stainer took him to the Cathedral of St. Paul, where there was a fine boys' choir.

The director welcomed them warmly and listened in amazement as John sang one difficult song after another, reading the notes easily as he went along.

"My dear sir, this young man is already a fine musician," exclaimed the director. "He reads better than any boy who has been singing in my choir for many long years. We would be happy, indeed, to have your son sing with us."

But John was not satisfied just to sing in the choir. He must learn to play on the organ, as well. At once the lessons began, and at fifteen he played with such skill that he was invited to be the organist of two London churches!

On he went to Oxford, to play the organ there. Why, this would be a good place to study, with the fine University at his very door! At once he set to work, and how proud he was, after long months of hard study, to receive the highest honors of the many students gathered there.

But a still greater honor came to him, when he was invited to go back to the Cathedral of St. Paul, to be the organist of the very church where he had sung as a boy of seven!

Never was anyone so busy! From sunup until dark, he did not stop writing his music books and hymns and playing on the organ. Queen Victoria was so pleased with his music that she made him a knight, and from that time on, he was known as Sir John Stainer.

Sometimes Sir John took old folk tunes and made them into beautiful songs. This one that he especially liked, was called "My Lady Greensleeves," and in olden times it was sung by the people as they danced on the village green:

"Alas my love, you do me wrong,   Greensleeves was all my joy,
  To cast me off discourteously,   Greensleeves was my delight,
  For I have loved you so long   Greensleeves was my heart of gold,
  Delighting in your company.   And all for my Lady Greensleeves."

Sir John Stainer took this quaint old folk tune, and with new words by the Englishman, William Dix, made the music for the carol, "What Child is This?" that we love to sing at Christmas time.

What Child is This?

WILLIAM C. DIX

Old English Air
"My Lady Greensleeves"

Moderato

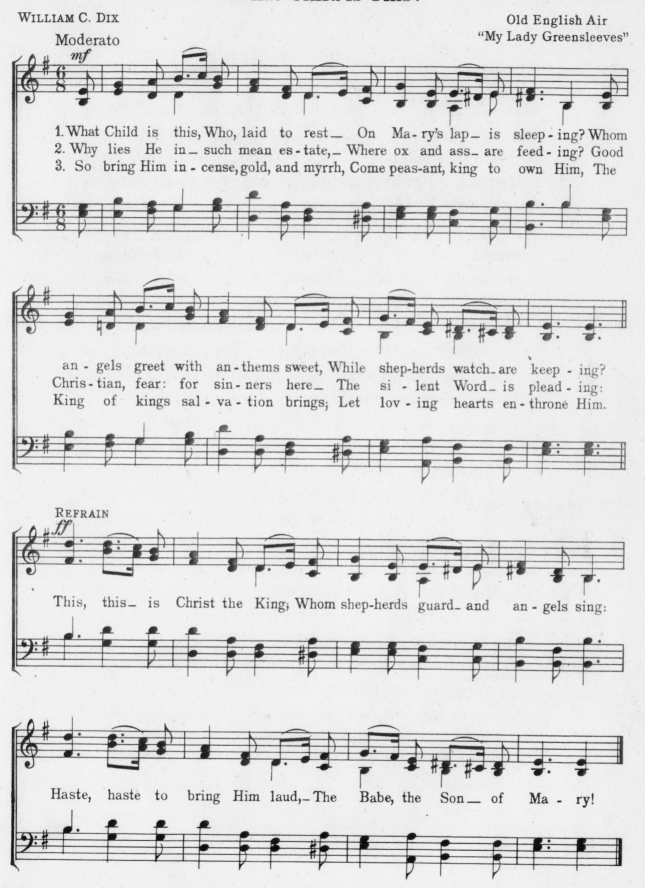

1. What Child is this, Who, laid to rest— On Ma-ry's lap— is sleep-ing? Whom
2. Why lies He in— such mean es-tate,— Where ox and ass— are feed-ing? Good
3. So bring Him in-cense, gold, and myrrh, Come peas-ant, king to own Him, The

an-gels greet with an-thems sweet, While shep-herds watch— are keep-ing?
Chris-tian, fear: for sin-ners here— The si-lent Word— is plead-ing:
King of kings sal-va-tion brings; Let lov-ing hearts en-throne Him.

REFRAIN

This, this— is Christ the King; Whom shep-herds guard— and an-gels sing:

Haste, haste to bring Him laud,—The Babe, the Son— of Ma-ry!

O HOLY NIGHT

HAPPY, laughing Paris was filled with fine musicians, playing and singing in every part of the great city, and for long weeks the young French boy, Adolphe Adam, had carefully saved every franc given him, until there was enough to take him to one of the beautiful concerts.

How he did love music! Far more than anything else, and whenever Father Adam was not practicing his compositions in the small piano room, Adolphe slipped in quietly to play by himself, and to make up little tunes.

Even though Father Adam was a well-known pianist and gave lessons at the famous school, the Paris Conservatory, he did not want his own son to study music, for he thought that the life of musicians was difficult, indeed.

"No, no, Adolphe – music is not for you," he would declare when the boy begged to work at the piano. "You must study hard to become a lawyer some day."

But Adolphe was not satisfied and he longed for music more than ever. There was only one thing left for him to do – he must teach himself to play. And so every afternoon, as soon as his lessons at the school were finished, he ran home as fast as his legs could carry him. Shutting himself away in the little piano room, he began to work slowly and patiently at the difficult pieces in his father's books.

For long months he worked alone until he was able to play every composition without a single mistake!

Late one evening as he sat struggling with a hard chord that would not come right, the door opened suddenly and there stood Father Adam.

"Adolphe! And how have you learned to play this difficult music?"

"I taught myself, Father."

To have mastered such a task, alone!

There was nothing to do now but to let the boy study in earnest, and in a few days, Adolphe joyously entered the music school where he was soon hard at work. The masters watched the new young pupil with astonishment, for never had anyone learned so fast.

But even more than playing on instruments, Adolphe liked to compose, and when the teacher Boieldieu came to the Conservatory, he found an eager young man awaiting him. Boieldieu was composing an opera and it was not long before his pupil was helping him, writing parts of the music himself.

Perhaps he could write an opera, too! Adolphe began at once, and when the beautiful work was finished, it was performed in Paris, delighting the large, eager audience.

Father Adam was pleased, indeed, and as opera after opera came from the pen of his son, he watched joyously as the new music was performed in Adolphe's own theater, set up with most of his hard-earned savings.

And now, how happy he was when the directors of the great Conservatory asked him to come there to teach young students how to write their music!

Besides operas, Adolphe Adam composed many other kinds of music. This song of his, "O Holy Night," is one of the most beautiful that we have to sing or to listen to, at Christmas time.

O Holy Night

(Cantique de Noël)

ADOLPHE ADAM

1. O ho-ly Night!_ the stars are bright-ly
2. Led by the light_ of faith se-rene-ly

shin — — ing, It is the night of the dear Sa-viour's
beam — — ing, With glow-ing hearts by His cra-dle we

birth.   Long lay the world_ in sin and er-ror
stand.   O'er all the world_ a star is sweet-ly

Fall_____ on your knees!_____ Oh, hear_____ the an-gel
Christ_____ is the Lord!_____ Then ev - - er, ev-er

voic - es! O night_____ di - vine,_____ the_____
praise we, His power_____ and glo - - ry_____

night_____ when Christ was born;   O   night,_____   O
ev - - er-more pro-claim!   His   pow'r_____   and

cresc.

ho - - ly   night,   O night di - vine!
glo - - ry   ev - - er-more pro-claim!

rall.

WHEN he was a very little boy in Olney, England, Henry Gauntlett loved to listen to the organ more than anything else in all the world. He lived in a house very near the church and whenever sounds of music came from the gray stone building, he ran on his short legs to the big doors to see who was playing.

Stealing down the long, dim aisle, he would crawl into a seat near the big pipes and listen wide-eyed to the music until the last sweet tones had died away. Many times, when Mother Gauntlett went to look for him, she found him fast asleep in the hard oaken pew.

As he grew older, he begged so hard to play on the organ that at last his father, half in fun, allowed him to take lessons on the instrument. To his great surprise, the young boy learned rapidly and spent all of his spare time in music.

Many times he wrote little melodies, and Father Gauntlett was delighted. He must help the boy to learn about the writing of music.

"Henry," he said one day, "Perhaps you would like to copy some compositions of the great masters. And for every one that is done correctly, you shall have a farthing."

To earn some money for his own! Henry ran to find pen and paper and a few days later, knocked at his father's door.

"Here, sir, are one thousand tunes that I have finished copying and I would like the payment now. But if it is too much money, I will settle for one guinea."

"One thousand tunes!" chuckled Father Gauntlett. "Very well, my son, you have earned the guinea. But perhaps you had better stop the copying for a time."

Father Gauntlett was eager to have better music in his church, so he promised the people that if they would buy a new organ, he would find the best musician in all the country-side to play it for them.

At once the people set to work and in a short time the men were ready to set up the new instrument. Henry watched eagerly and then ran to find his father.

"Oh, sir, I would like to be the organist in the church," he cried. "And the charge for my services would be so little, that it would pay you to hire me, Father."

"But the music is far too difficult, my son," explained Father Gauntlett, looking down at the eager, nine-year-old boy. "But some time, when you are able to play the long service, you shall be the organist."

There was no time to lose! From early morning until night Henry struggled with the compositions and when at last the organ was installed, he was able to play every note of the difficult music without a mistake. Father Gauntlett could not believe his ears!

"Very well, my fine young musician. You shall be the first to perform on our beautiful new instrument, for the position of organist is yours."

Never was a boy so happy, and for eleven long years Henry played the organ in his father's church, delighting everyone with his music. And from that time on, Henry Gauntlett spent the rest of his life in composing music for the church. For the poem written by Mrs. Alexander, he wrote the music for the lovely "Once in Royal David's City."

Once in Royal David's City

MRS. CECIL FRANCES ALEXANDER

HENRY J. GAUNTLETT

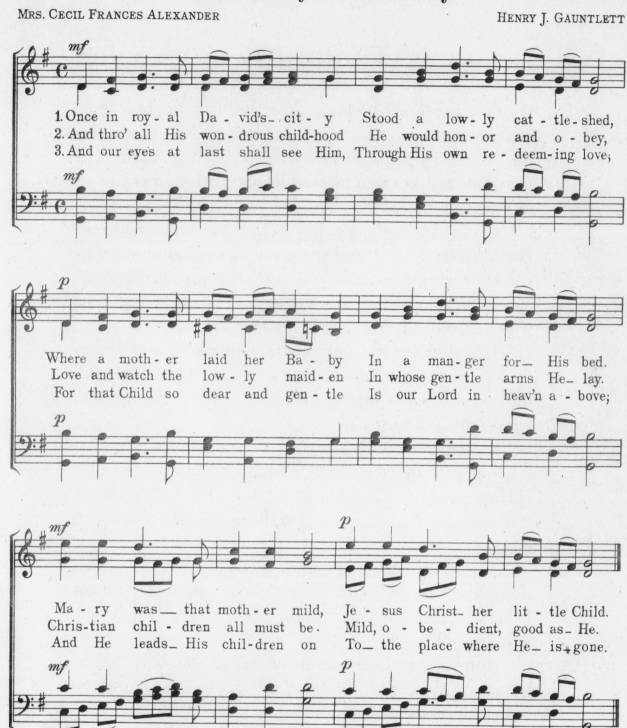

1. Once in roy-al Da-vid's cit-y Stood a low-ly cat-tle-shed,
2. And thro' all His won-drous child-hood He would hon-or and o-bey,
3. And our eyes at last shall see Him, Through His own re-deem-ing love;

Where a moth-er laid her Ba-by In a man-ger for His bed.
Love and watch the low-ly maid-en In whose gen-tle arms He lay.
For that Child so dear and gen-tle Is our Lord in heav'n a-bove;

Ma-ry was that moth-er mild, Je-sus Christ her lit-tle Child.
Chris-tian chil-dren all must be. Mild, o-be-dient, good as He.
And He leads His chil-dren on To the place where He is gone.

4.
For He is our childhood's pattern;
  Day by day like us He grew;
He was little, weak, and helpless,
  Tears and smiles like us He knew;
And He feeleth for our sadness,
And He shareth in our gladness.

5.
Not in that poor lowly stable,
  With the oxen standing by,
We shall see Him, but in heaven,
  Set at God's right hand on high;
When like stars His children crowned,
All in white shall wait around.

ON THE day before Christmas, there was no busier household in all the German countryside than that of the Luthers. Besides the many preparations for the festival day, there were the children to be cared for, and by nightfall Mother Luther was weary, indeed.

"Come, dear wife, surely you have earned a good rest. Now I shall take the burdens on my own broad shoulders," said Martin Luther, kindly. And turning to his merrily-romping children, he added, with a twinkle in his eye, "And those who are speedily in bed shall have a song or a story."

The scrambling and scurrying brought chuckles to the lips of Father Luther. Before many minutes had passed, the children were all safely in bed, snuggling under warm blankets against the cold winter night.

"A song! A story! It's time for the song!"

From its hook on the wall, Father Luther took down his old lute, and seating himself beside the cradle, he rocked little Paul and sang Christmas songs in the light of the great open hearth.

At last there was not a sound, as one by one the children dropped off to sleep. All but little Paul, who watched his father with clear blue eyes, shining like star-bells from the low wooden cradle.

"And you, my little one of the seeing eyes, why do you not sleep? Are you waiting for the Christmas dawn to come creeping in at the window?"

There was no sound but the gentle rocking through the fire-lit room, and Luther thought of the Christ Child, cradled in a manger in Bethlehem, so long ago. As he sat there dreaming, a song came into his mind, and lightly strumming the melody, he sang the words as they came to him:

> "From heaven high I come to you,
> To bring you tiding good and true."

Little Paul seemed to like the new song and smiling up at his father, he closed his blue eyes and fell fast asleep. As the verses went on, Martin Luther set them down with a strong, stirring melody. Now the children would have a new song for Christmas!

And on Christmas day, not only his own little ones gathered around him, but the neighbor children, as well. With glowing cheeks and snowflakes fresh on their fair hair, they bounded into the cheery Luther home, calling their merry greetings.

"Sing for us, Herr Luther! Sing for Christmas!"

"Ah, my merry little ones, and today you shall have a surprise. There is a new Christmas song that I wrote for Paul last night."

With shining eyes, the children listened to the lovely deep voice of Martin Luther as he sang the new carol, "From Heaven High I Come to You." Soon the sweet young voices were singing the song in clear ringing tones.

Martin Luther listened carefully, a smile of joy lighting his kindly face as he accompanied them on the lute.

"Ah, my children, what a wonderful gift is music! It comes to us from the very gates of heaven!"

As the merry songsters danced away through the Christmas storm, bits of the lovely hymn floated back into the Luther home:

> "From heaven high I come to you,
> To bring you tiding good and true."

From Heaven High I Come to You

MARTIN LUTHER

1. From Heav - en high___ I come to you, To bring you
2. This King is but___ a lit - tle child, His moth - er
3. Now let us all___ with songs of cheer, Fol - low the

tid - ings___ good___ and true. Good tid - ings of___ great
bless - ed___ Ma - ry mild. His cra - dle is___ but
shep - herds and___ draw near, To find this won - drous

joy I___ bring, To you this night is___ born___ a King.
now a___ stall, Yet He brings joy and___ peace to all.
gift of___ Heav'n, The bless - ed Christ whom God___ hath giv'n.

LULLY, LULLY, LU

Since early Christmas morning, the little English town of Chester had been bustling with preparations so that by mid-afternoon all would be in readiness for the Mystery Plays to be given in the market square.

The town children had been up with the sun, for this was the most special time in all the year, when stories from the life of Christ were played for the people.

Already twenty-four double stages on wheels had been drawn in by strong horses and placed around the open square. With joyous shouts the children ran from one to the other, holding curtains while they were nailed in place, carrying costumes, and helping in whatever way they could.

When the sun was high overhead, the many tasks were finished and near the carts, large crowds had gathered, for it was almost time for the performances to begin.

Suddenly the trumpet call sounded, loud and clear and, with excited cries and hand-clapping from the children, the curtains of the first cart were drawn aside.

There were the musicians, led by the chief player, his left hand pumping the bellows of the little organ strapped around his neck, while with his right, he played favorite Christmas carols.

Round and round the small platform they marched, the singing angels following, their wings and long hair of bright gold shining in the sun. There was deep silence as Mary, with the Christ Child in her arms, rode over the stage on a sturdy little donkey while the music played softly the quiet lullaby carol, "Lully, Lully, Lu."

Down went the curtains, and in the twinkling of an eye, the actors arranged the first scene while the musicians played outside for the people to sing. When all was ready, the trumpet call sounded again and slowly the curtains were pulled aside.

There, before the delighted people, was the manger scene with Mary and the Christ Child; and the shepherds, bearing their simple gifts. While Joseph watched patiently by her side, Mary sat beside the crib, sweetly singing the quaint old song, "Lully, Lully, Lu," that had come from Italy so many years before.

When the last sweet sounds of the lovely carol had died away, the people applauded again and again, for of all the Mystery Plays, this was their favorite.

And they must still have more Christmas music, so off the stage and through the streets went the players, up and down and around the town, followed by the people, all lustily singing their beloved Christmas carols.

The Mystery Plays became very famous, indeed. Sometimes even kings and queens journeyed many long miles to see them when they were performed on large, well-built stages, with beautiful scenery and specially trained actors.

And today, more than five hundred years later, we still sing the old carol, "Lully, Lully, Lu," sometimes called "The Carol of the Nuns of St. Mary's." And you may be sure that never a year passes that the good nuns of St. Mary's, in the Cathedral of Chester, do not use this beautiful carol in their Christmas processionals.

Lully, Lully, Lu

Latin Carol
15th Century

1. Christ, the Babe was giv'n to all___ Lul-ly, lul-ly, lu!___
2. Jo-seph brought the swad-dling clothes Bye, bye, bye, bye, bye.___
3. Cra-dled in the soft mown hay___ Lul-ly, lul-ly, lu!___

Born in low-ly man-ger stall, Bye, bye, bye, bye, bye.___
Ma-ry wrapped the Babe so dear, Lul-ly, lul-ly, lu.___
There the gen-tle Christ Child lay, Bye, bye, bye, bye, bye.___

Born to reign a-bove us all___ Lul-ly, lul-ly, lu!___
Ly-ing in the man-ger near___ Bye, bye, bye, bye, bye.___
On that bless-ed Christ-mas day___ Lul-ly, lul-ly, lu!___

ANGELS WE HAVE HEARD ON HIGH

LONG, long ago in Rome, in the year 129, there lived a good bishop, named Telesphorus. Now Bishop Telesphorus wanted the people to celebrate the birth of the Christ Child, so each year, as Christmas time drew near, he sent forth his command:

"Good citizens, on the Holy Night of the Nativity of our Lord and Saviour, you will attend services in the church, and solemnly sing the Angels' Hymn, because on this same night, He was declared unto the shepherds by an angel, as the truth itself doth witness."

The voices of the people rang joyously in all the churches as they sang the beautiful Latin hymn, "Gloria in Excelsis Deo," which means, "Glory to God in the Highest."

This Latin hymn was the very first Christmas song ever to be sung by all of the people together, throughout the land. And even today, we are still singing a part of the same hymn in the refrain of "Angels We Have Heard on High," which is: "Gloria in Excelsis Deo." The verse part of the carol is an old French melody.

Angels We Have Heard on High

Translated

Old French Melody

1. An - gels we have heard on high, Sweet - ly sing - ing o'er the plains;
2. Shep - herds, why this ju - bi - lee? Why your joy - ous songs pro - long?
3. Come to Beth - le - hem, and see Him whose birth the an - gels sing;

And the moun - tains in re - ply Ech - o - ing their joy - ous strains.
What the glad - some tid - ings be Which in - spire your heav'n - ly song?
Come a - dore on bend - ed knee, Christ, the Lord, our new - born King.

REFRAIN

Glo - - - - - - - ri - a

in ex - cel - sis De - o, — Glo - - - - -

- ri - a in ex - cel - sis De - - o. —

O Come, Little Children

J. P. A. SCHULZ

1. O come little children, O come one and all. The cradle is here as in Bethlehem's stall. And see what the Father, from high Heav'n above, Has sent us to-night as a proof of His love.

2. O see in the cradle this night in the stall, See here wondrous light that is dazzling to all. In clean lovely white lies the Heavenly Child, Not even the angels are more sweet and mild.

3. O there He lies, children, asleep in the hay, While Mary and Joseph watch Him happily. The shepherds are praying before His rude bed, Their sweet songs are singing, by angels they're led.

Good Christian Men, Rejoice

John Mason Neale

Old German

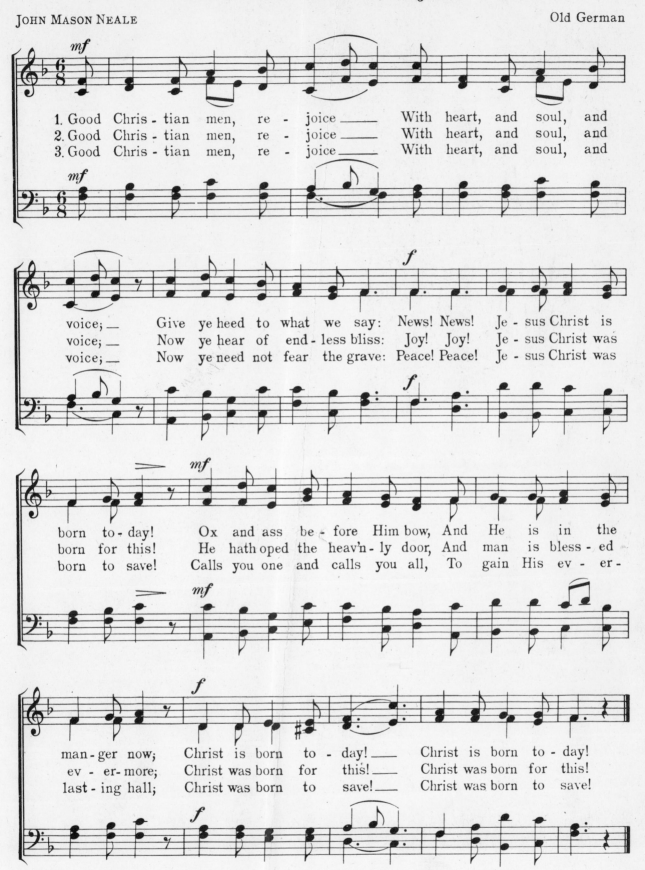

1. Good Chris - tian men, re - joice____ With heart, and soul, and
2. Good Chris - tian men, re - joice____ With heart, and soul, and
3. Good Chris - tian men, re - joice____ With heart, and soul, and

voice; ____ Give ye heed to what we say: News! News! Je - sus Christ is
voice; ____ Now ye hear of end - less bliss: Joy! Joy! Je - sus Christ was
voice; ____ Now ye need not fear the grave: Peace! Peace! Je - sus Christ was

born to - day! Ox and ass be - fore Him bow, And He is in the
born for this! He hath oped the heav'n - ly door, And man is bless - ed
born to save! Calls you one and calls you all, To gain His ev - er -

man - ger now; Christ is born to - day! ____ Christ is born to - day!
ev - er - more; Christ was born for this! ____ Christ was born for this!
last - ing hall; Christ was born to save! ____ Christ was born to save!